Blueprints Science: Key Stage 1

BARCLAY INFANTS SCHOOL
CANTERBURY ROAD
LEYTON E10 6EJ

Copymasters

BLUEPRINTS

Science
Key Stage 1
Copymasters

Second Edition

Jim Fitzsimmons

Rhona Whiteford

Stanley Thornes (Publishers) Ltd

BLUEPRINTS – HOW TO GET MORE INFORMATION

Blueprints is an expanding series of practical teacher's ideas books and photocopiable resources for use in primary schools. Books are available for every Key Stage of every core and foundation subject, as well as for an ever widening range of other primary needs. **Blueprints** are carefully structured around the demands of National Curriculum but may be used successfully by schools and teachers not following the National Curriculum in England and Wales.

Blueprints provide:

- Total National Curriculum coverage
- Hundreds of practical ideas
- Books specifically for the Key Stage you teach
- Flexible resources for the whole school or for individual teachers
- Excellent photocopiable sheets – ideal for assessment, SATs and children's work profiles
- Supreme value.

Books may be bought by credit card over the telephone and information obtained on (0242) 228888. Alternatively, photocopy and return this FREEPOST form to join our mailing list. We will mail you regularly with information on new and existing titles.

Please add my name to the BLUEPRINTS mailing list. *Photocopiable*

Name _____

Address_____

_____

_____

Postcode_____

To: Marketing Services Dept., Stanley Thornes Publishers, FREEPOST (GR 782), Cheltenham, Glos. GL53 1BR

First published in 1990 as Blueprints Science 5–7 Copymasters
Reprinted 1991.
Reprinted 1992.
Second edition published in 1992 by
Stanley Thornes (Publishers) Ltd
Ellenborough House
Wellington Street
CHELTENHAM GL50 1YD

Reprinted 1993 (twice)

A catalogue record for this book is available from the British Library.

ISBN 0–7487–1492–8

Typeset by Tech-Set, Gateshead, Tyne & Wear.

CONTENTS

Introduction

Copymasters 1–94

Record Sheets 1–6

Record Sheets 1–2: AT1
Record Sheets 3–6: ATs 2–4

INTRODUCTION

In this book there are 94 photocopiable copymasters linked to many of the activities in the Teacher's Resource Book. Where the copymasters are referred to in the text of the Teacher's Resource Book there are some instructions on how to use them. They are referred to by number in the Teacher' Resource Book by this symbol: . The copymasters give the children a chance to record activities and results in an organised way, and in some cases to consolidate learning that has gone before. When the children have completed these copymasters they can be added to workfiles or used as exemplar materials in pupils profiles. You may also wish to use completed copymasters as a resource for your assessments. There are two record sheets at the back of this book, on which you can note which copymasters the children have made use of, and their experience of work contributing to AT1.

At the top of each copymaster you will find symbols that explain how that sheet contributes to work on the all important Attainment Target 1: Scientific investigation. These symbols are explained in detail in the Teacher's Resource Book but they are set out here for ready reference.

Level 1
Observation   Discussion

Level 2
Observation   Discussion   Ask questions   Identify   Measure   List   Record findings   Interpret findings

Level 3
Observation   Discussion   Formulate hypotheses   Identify   Fair/unfair test   Use instruments   Quantify variables   Record

Interpret charts   Interpret and generalise   Sequence

Copymasters
1–94

My favourite TV programme

Talking to someone a long way away C2

typewriter

telephone

television

record player

two-way radio

telephone box

Circle or colour the things you could use.

I spy aerials

C3

I can see [ ] aerials.

Passing on visual information

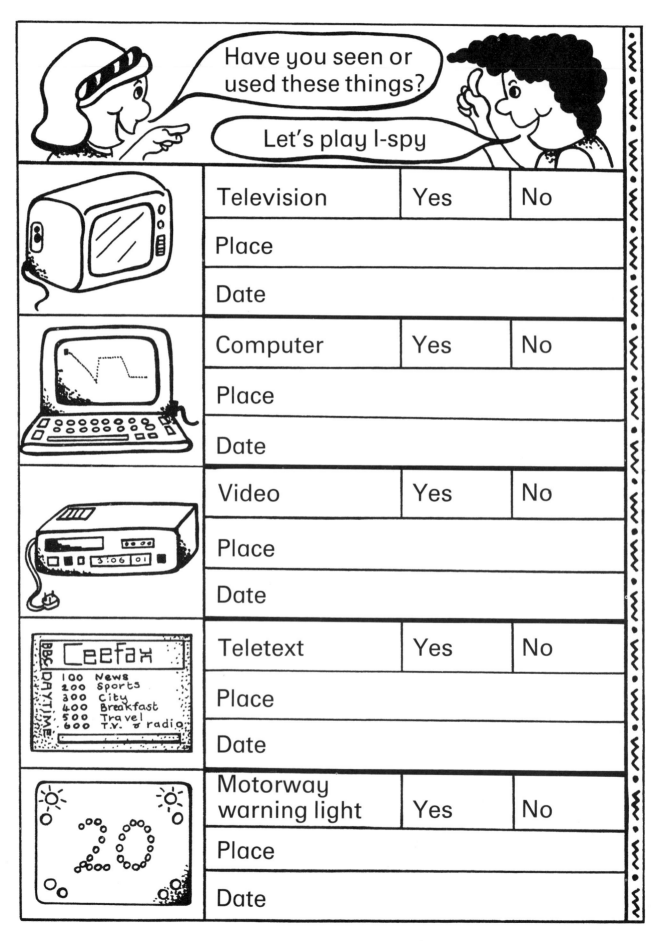

	Television	Yes	No
	Place		
	Date		
	Computer	Yes	No
	Place		
	Date		
	Video	Yes	No
	Place		
	Date		
	Teletext	Yes	No
	Place		
	Date		
	Motorway warning light	Yes	No
	Place		
	Date		

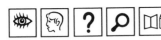

Passing on audio information

 C5

Have you seen or used these things?

Have you?

	Radio	Yes	No
	Place		
	Date		

	Tape recorder	Yes	No
	Place		
	Date		

	Record player	Yes	No
	Place		
	Date		

	CD player	Yes	No
	Place		
	Date		

	Telephone	Yes	No
	Place		
	Date		

Storing information

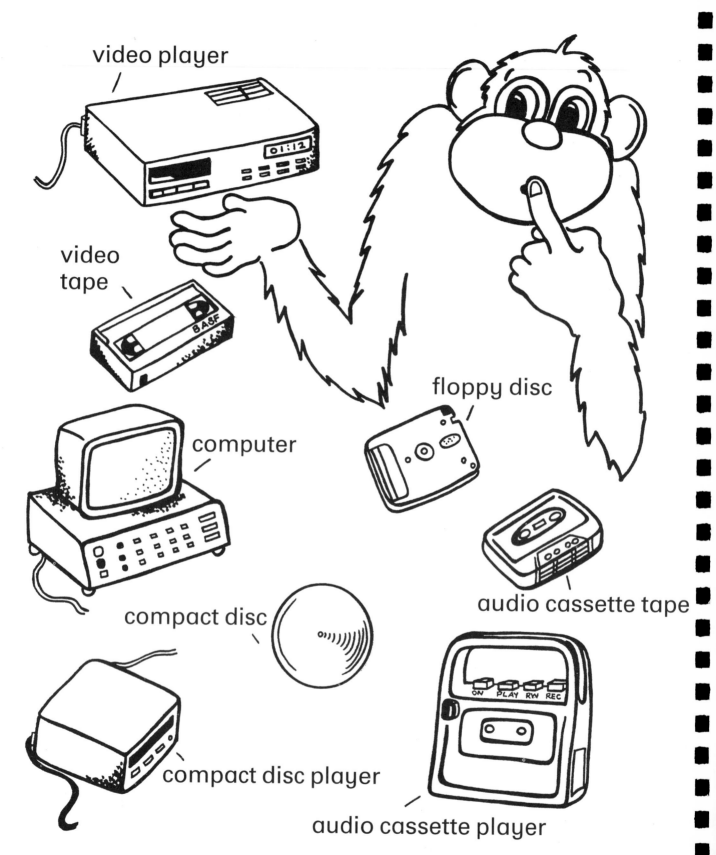

video player

video tape

computer

floppy disc

compact disc

compact disc player

audio cassette tape

audio cassette player

Match the machine to the disc or tape it uses.

Using a tape recorder

C7

Making a recording: Number the correct order.

Check microphone

Press play

Stop

Press 'record'

Plug in/Switch on

Make recording

Insert tape correctly

Rewind

Listen to recording

Rainbow body

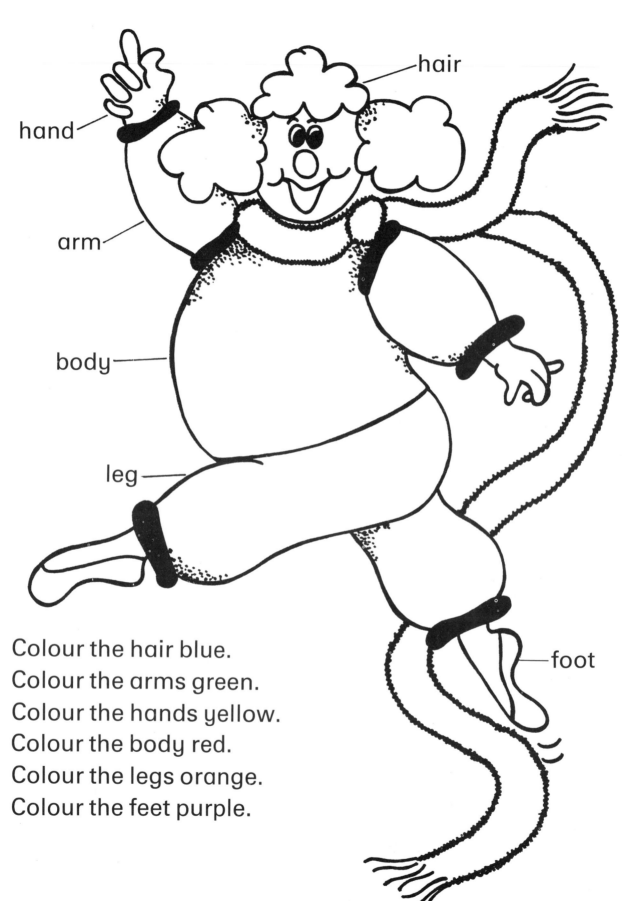

hair

hand

arm

body

leg

foot

Colour the hair blue.
Colour the arms green.
Colour the hands yellow.
Colour the body red.
Colour the legs orange.
Colour the feet purple.

Things I do with my body

C9

writing

reading

dancing

swimming

painting

running

listening

watching

Plants

Write the names of the different parts of the plants.

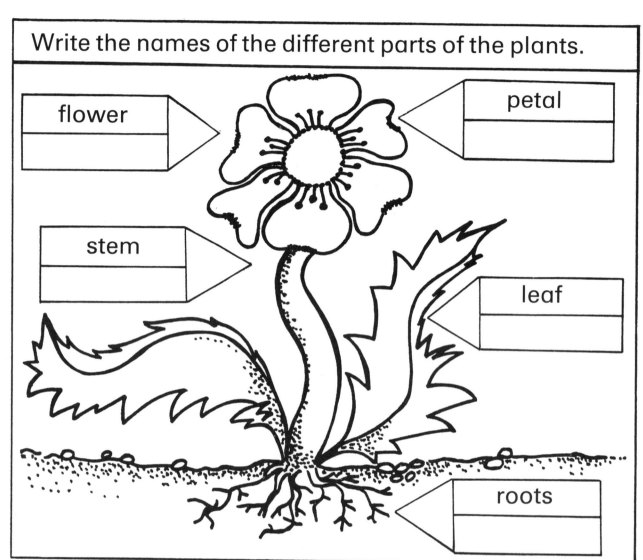

flower

petal

stem

leaf

roots

Finish off the picture.

Living and non-living

Make a set of the drawings of living things and colour them in.

Our walk

 C12

On our walk

I saw

I smelt

I heard

I felt

I tasted

People

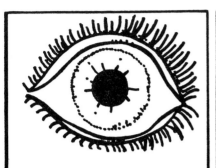

My eyes are

My hair is

My skin is

This is me.

These people live in my house.

What do plants need?

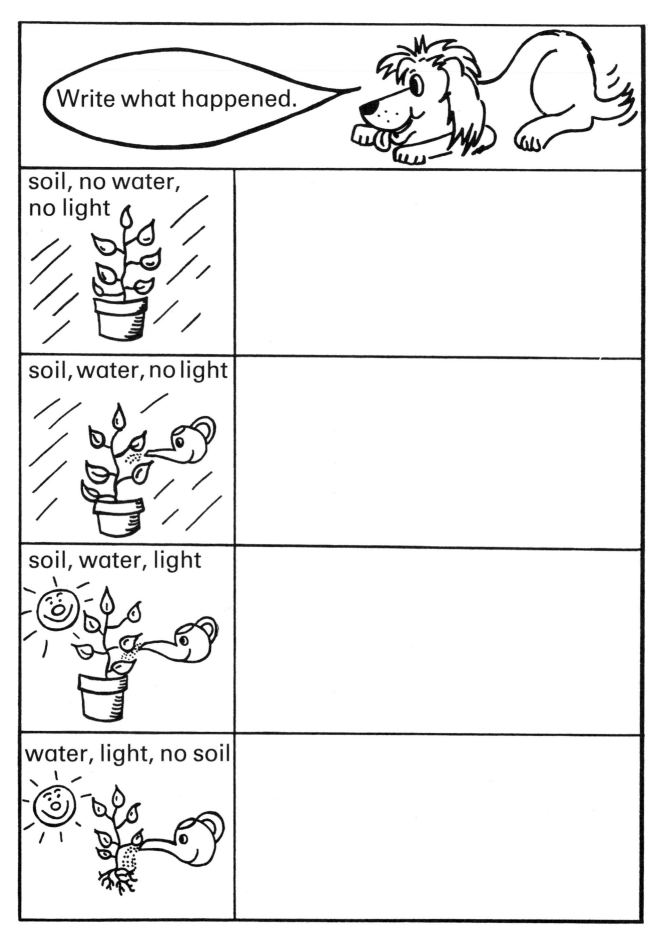

Write what happened.

soil, no water, no light

soil, water, no light

soil, water, light

water, light, no soil

What do animals need?

C15

This is a _____

| mammal | bird | fish | reptile | amphibian | other |

What it likes

| warmth | cold | light | dark |

Where it lives

| mountain | plain | jungle/wood | underground | underwater |

What food it likes

| plants | animals | both |

Who it lives with

| alone | family | herd |

Caring for pets

C16

This is my pet _____

water

feeding

exercise

cleaning out

grooming

training and play

Changes

C17

Write and draw what happened.

We put the seedlings in a hot oven.

Temperature   °C

We put the seedlings on a table in our classroom.

Temperature   °C

We put the seedlings in the freezer overnight.

Temperature   °C

Are you a boy or a girl?

C18

is a girl.

is a boy.

Faces

This is me.

Things I am good at

Colour or circle the activities you can do.

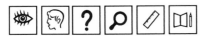
All about me

Name		Age	Sex

Place of birth

Height	cm	Weight	kg

Colour of eyes _____

Colour of skin _____

Colour of hair _____

Shoe size

Other facts

Elements of a graph

I can do this

I am _____ cm tall.

I can reach up to _____ cm.

I can leap up to _____ cm.

I can jump _____ cm.

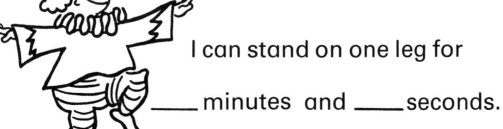

I can stand on one leg for

_____ minutes and _____ seconds.

Mr Litter

Colour the things you found.

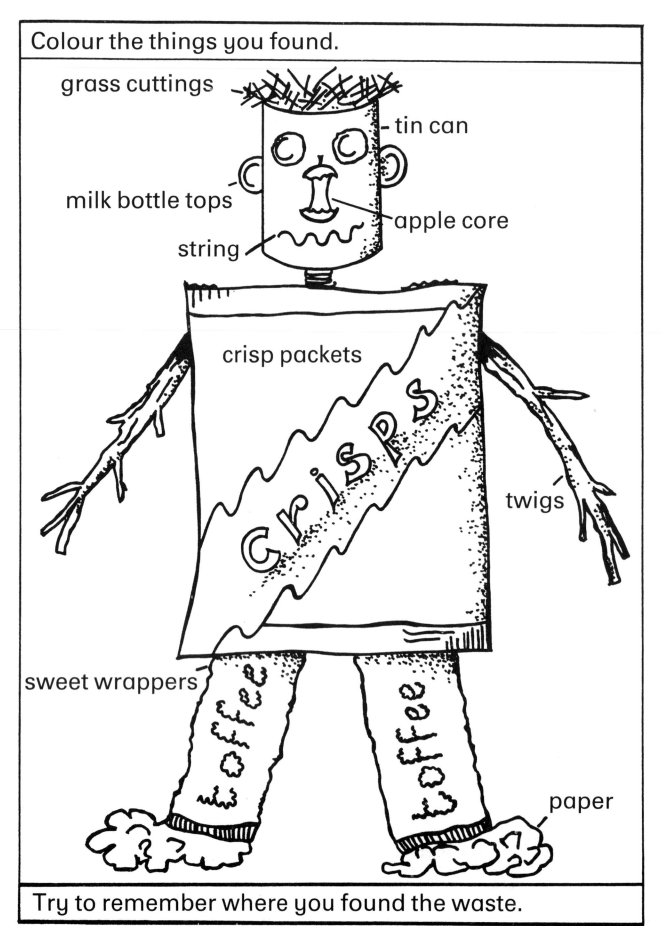

grass cuttings

tin can

milk bottle tops

apple core

string

crisp packets

twigs

sweet wrappers

paper

Try to remember where you found the waste.

Where did it come from?

Match the pictures.

Where is it?

HIG SONS LTD.

Draw a ring around the waste.

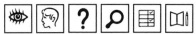
Rubbish collection

C27

Natural materials

Man-made materials

Mixtures

What rots?

The material tested

This material was put in these places.

Place	Week 1	Week 2	Week 3
In the air outside			
In the air inside			
In water			
In garden soil			
In sand			
In wet peat			

Prehistoric life

land dinosaur	flying dinosaur	marine dinosaur

Name of dinosaur

Where it lived

What it ate

Other information

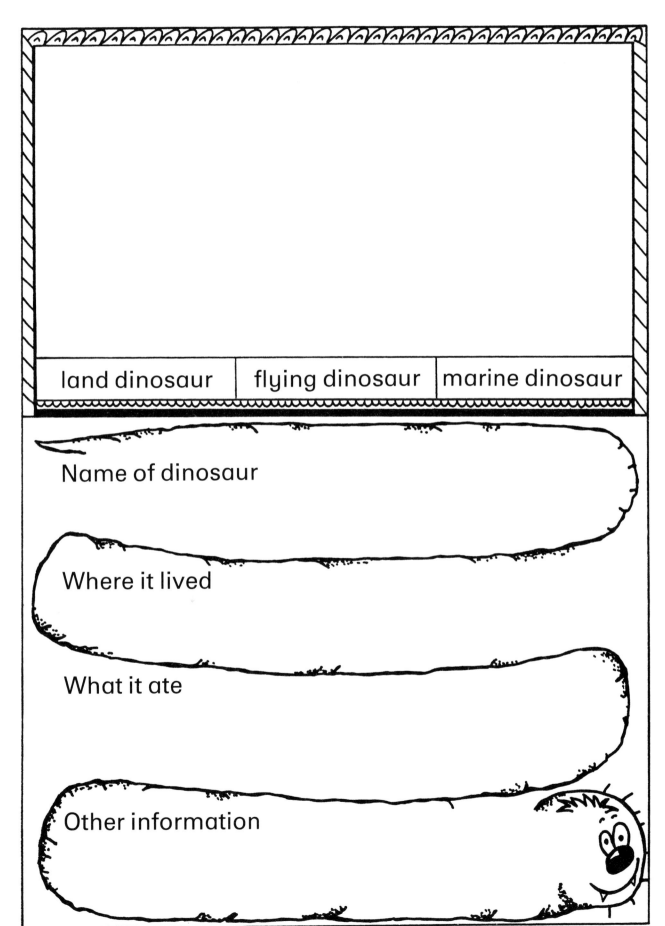

Diary

1.

Date _____

2.

Date _____

3.

Date _____

4.

Date _____

5.

Date _____

6.

Date _____

Can you match the families?

c _ _ _	l _ _ _	b _ _ _
e _ _	f _ _ _	h _ _
c _ _ _ _	m _ _ _	r _ _
c _ _	c _ _ _	s _ _ _ _ _ _ _

Horses	**Cattle**	**Chickens**	**Sheep**
stallion	bull	cock	ram
mare	cow	hen	ewe
foal	calf	chick	lamb
red	blue	yellow	green

Taking care of yourself

Name of person?

Food	What foods do you usually have for:
	breakfast _____
	lunch _____
	tea _____
	supper _____

Sleep

What time do you go to bed? _____

What time do you get up? _____

How many hours' sleep do you have each night? _____ hours

Exercise

Tick if you do these things in the week.

walk	run	skip	play
ride a bike	skate		swim
play football	ride a horse		others

Hygiene

Number of washes each day _____

Number of times teeth cleaned each day _____

Number of baths in a week _____

I think I am 😊   I am not 😟 healthy.

My day

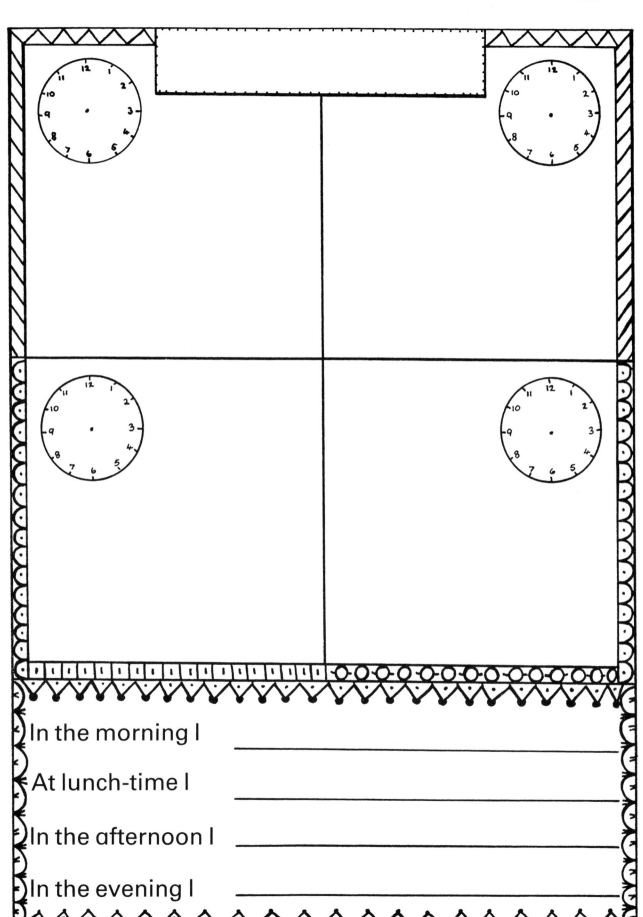

In the morning I _____

At lunch-time I _____

In the afternoon I _____

In the evening I _____

We are what we eat

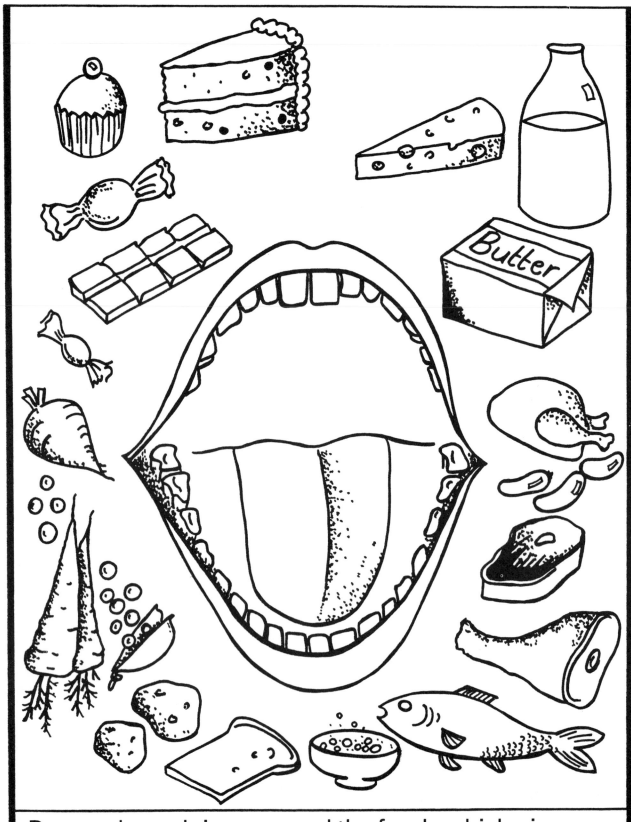

Draw coloured rings around the foods which give us energy (red), build our bodies (blue), clean us out (green).

The food we eat

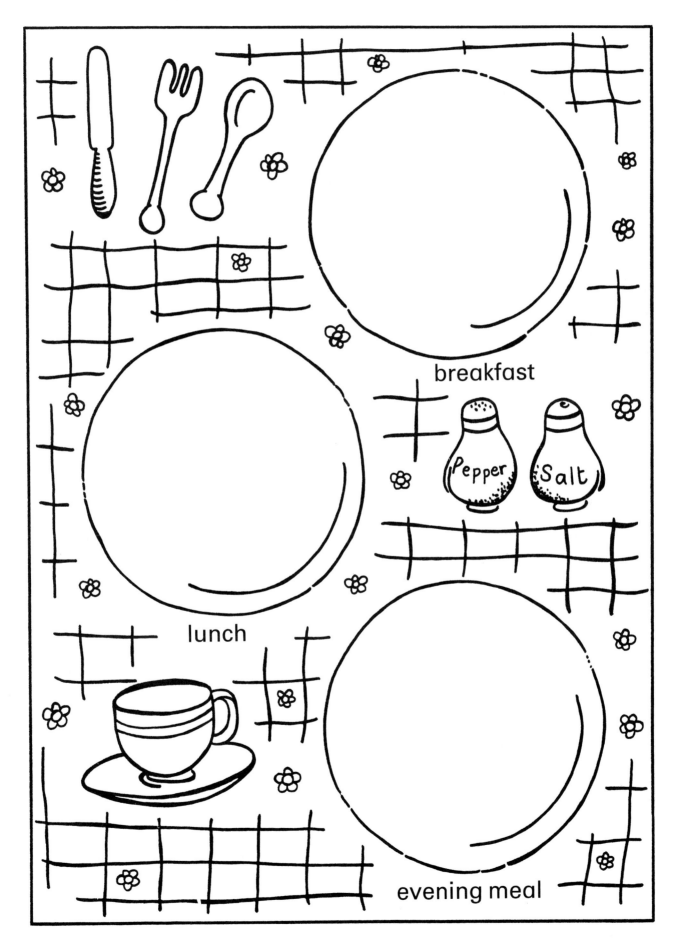

breakfast

Pepper   Salt

lunch

evening meal

All living things need food

Match the animal with its food.

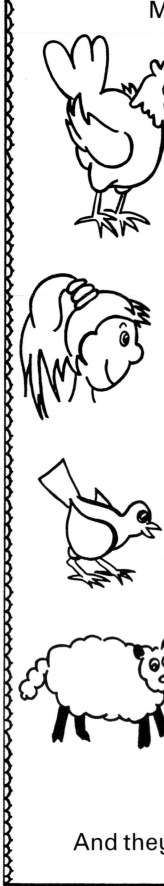

And they **all** need water.

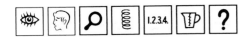

What is it?

C37

This is a

Feeding	Breathing

Movement	Behaviour

Habitat

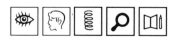

Our neighbourhood

Human activity	How these activities affect our neighbourhood
Industry	
Agriculture	
Mining	
Houses	
Parks	
Motorways	
Airports	
Cars	
Oil refinery/ power stations	
Reservoirs	
Other	

Materials I found

This is smooth.

This is rough.

This is hard.

This is soft.

This is bumpy.

This is spongy.

This is slippery.

This is sticky.

This is squashy.

Look at shapes

Finish off the picture.

Complete the patterns.

Fruit colours

Colour these fruits.

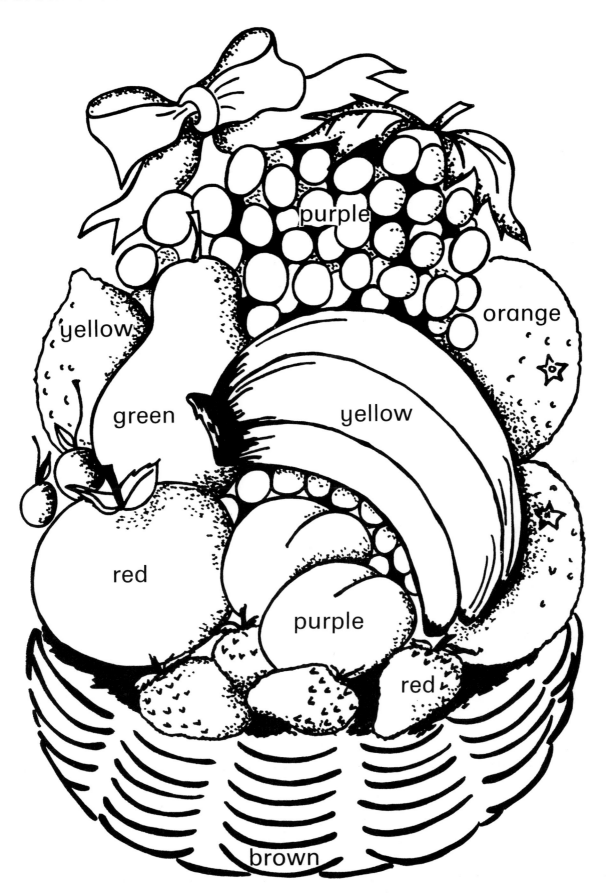

Looking at materials

C42

Properties	The materials we looked at						
	iron	rock	glass	wood	paper	fabric	plastic
hard							
soft							
rough							
smooth							
rigid							
flexible							
shiny							
dull							
transparent							
translucent							
opaque							
fixed shape							
malleable							
bounces							
does not bounce							

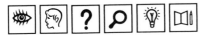

Grouping materials

Window

1. _____
2. _____
3. _____

Roof

1. _____
2. _____
3. _____

Door

1. _____
2. _____
3. _____

Wall

1. _____
2. _____
3. _____

What is it?

Animal

Vegetable

Mineral

Sort these things into three sets.

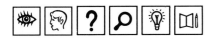

Changes

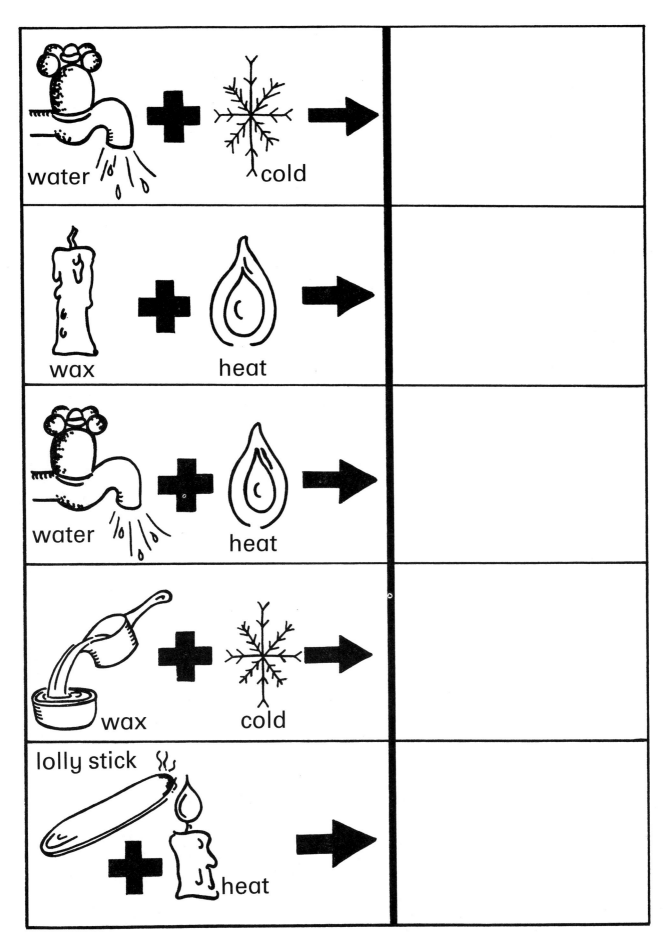

water + cold →	
wax + heat →	
water + heat →	
wax + cold →	
lolly stick + heat →	

Comparing materials

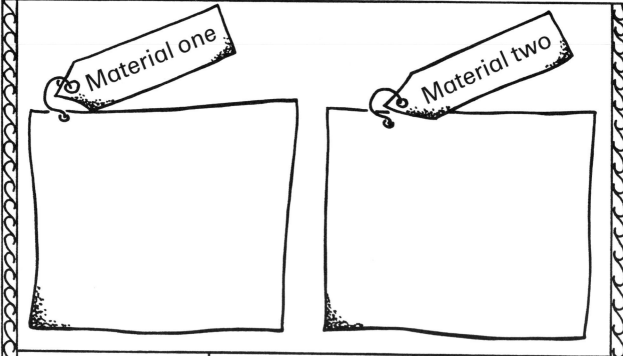

Material one

Material two

Differences	Similarities	Differences

Weathering

C47

Site	Damage	Possible cause

Static electricity

I rubbed a balloon on my head. Static electricity on the balloon picked up these things.

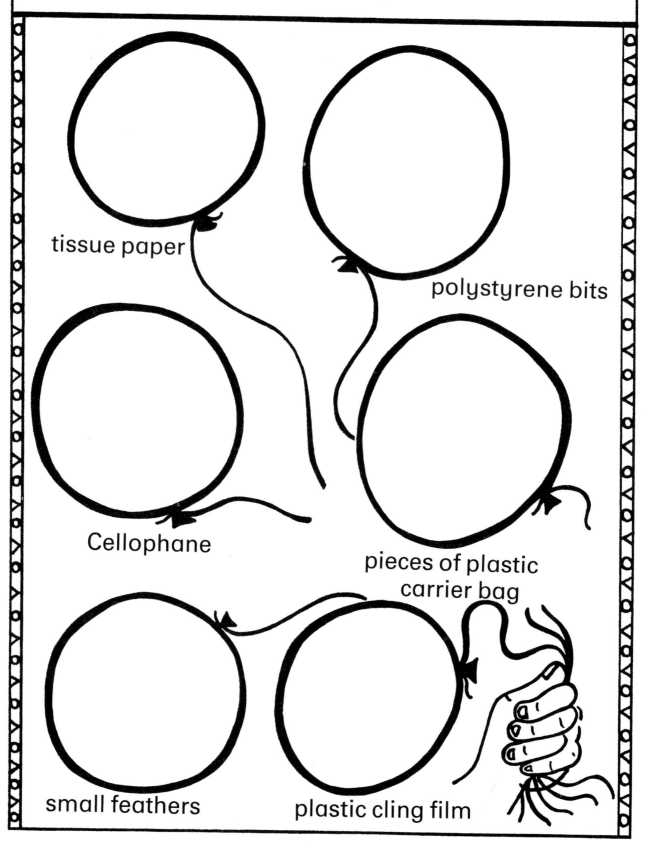

tissue paper

polystyrene bits

Cellophane

pieces of plastic
carrier bag

small feathers

plastic cling film

bedroom	bathroom
lounge	kitchen/dining room

Dangers from electricity

Danger

Repair worn flex.

Don't poke in sockets.

Switch off when not in use.

Don't touch electrical things with wet hands.

Don't use electrical equipment in the bathroom.

Don't overload sockets.

Look out for

Danger!

Join the warning to the correct picture.

How did you push these things?

Draw a blue line round the things you pushed with your hand and arm.
Draw a red line round the things you pushed with your leg and foot.
Draw a green line round the things you pushed with your whole body.

The mighty wind race

Water pushes things

C54

Which of these things could you push with your jet of water?
Tick if the water pushed it.
Cross if the water could not push it.

plastic bucket

feather

ping-pong ball

football

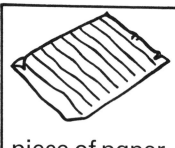

piece of paper

piece of wood

toy car

waste bin

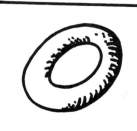

quoit

Pushing and pulling

C55

I do these things when I am:

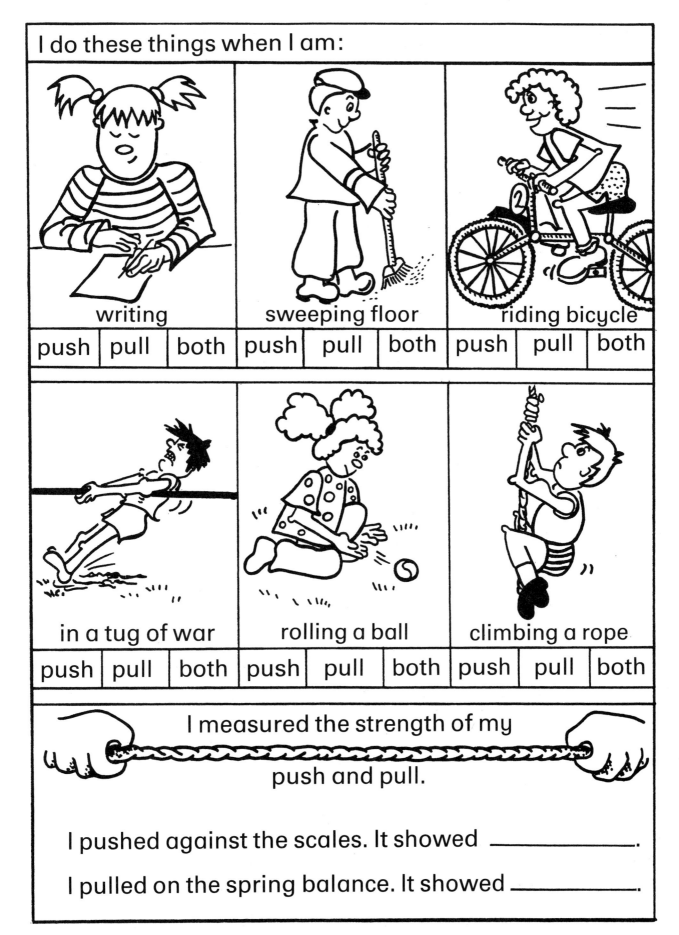

writing

push	pull	both

sweeping floor

push	pull	both

riding bicycle

push	pull	both

in a tug of war

push	pull	both

rolling a ball

push	pull	both

climbing a rope

push	pull	both

I measured the strength of my push and pull.

I pushed against the scales. It showed _____.

I pulled on the spring balance. It showed _____.

Downy duckling's walk

Can you make the sounds of the things I saw?

Downy duckling walked out in the sunshine.

He saw a little bee on a flower.

He saw a grey cat washing his fur.

He saw a tree blown in the wind.

He saw a fire engine  in the road.

He saw a dog in a garden.

He saw raindrops falling on his nose.

He waddled quickly to the farmyard and
he saw his mum looking for him. So he hurried home.

"Quack quack", he said.

How I made a sound on this instrument

C57

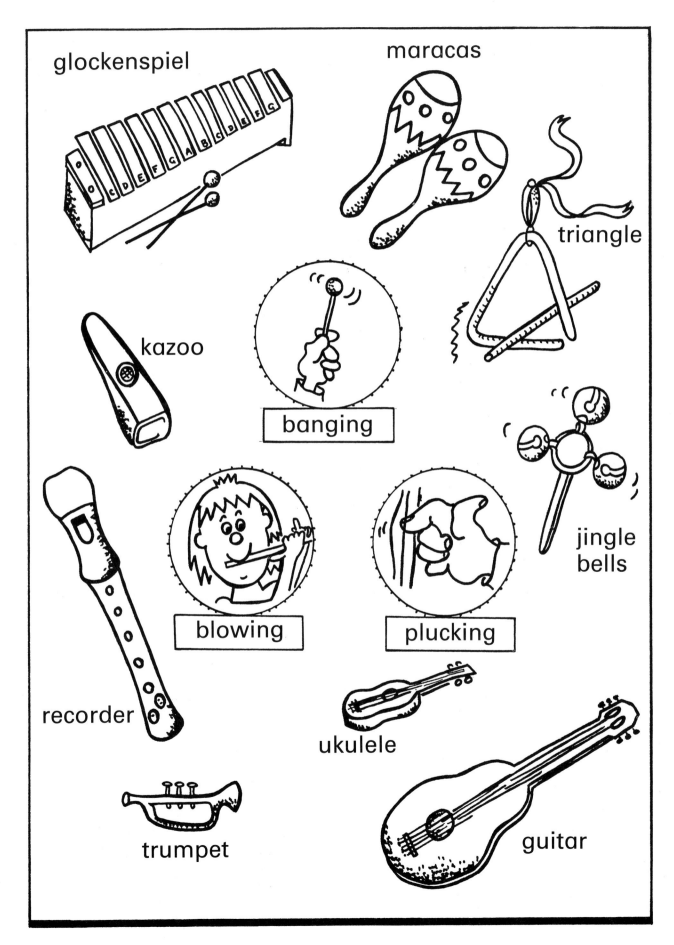

glockenspiel

maracas

triangle

kazoo

banging

recorder

blowing

plucking

jingle bells

ukulele

trumpet

guitar

Sounds

C58

Which was loudest?   Number it 1.

Which was softest?   Number it 5.

Put them in order 1 to 5.

	Put a number here
lorry rushing	
wind	
feather falling	
dog barking	
bird singing	

Hearing sounds

C59

How well can you hear these things?				
	close to	far away	in another room	with other noise
blowing recorder				
shouting				
radio				
talking				
beating drum				
spoon and glass				
→	Can hear	✓	Cannot hear	✗

Picking up sounds

C60

♫ ♩ ♫ ♩ ♩ ♩ ♫ ♩	with ear cups	without
whistle	_____ metres	_____ metres
whisper	_____ metres	_____ metres
triangle	_____ metres	_____ metres
cymbals	_____ metres	_____ metres
shout	_____ metres	_____ metres

in front	behind	left side	right side

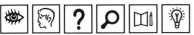
Making sounds

How can you make sounds with these instruments?

tambourine 	guitar
recorder	drum
claves	glockenspiel

| shake | strike | pluck | blow | beat |

Sounds and materials

plastic bag

Type of box

_____

Material used

_____

Plasticine	newspaper	thick woolly jumper	tin foil
cotton wool	plastic bags	wood shavings	sand

What I did

What I discovered

Lights

Draw a ring around the places where light comes from.

Mixing colours

brown	green	purple	turquoise	orange

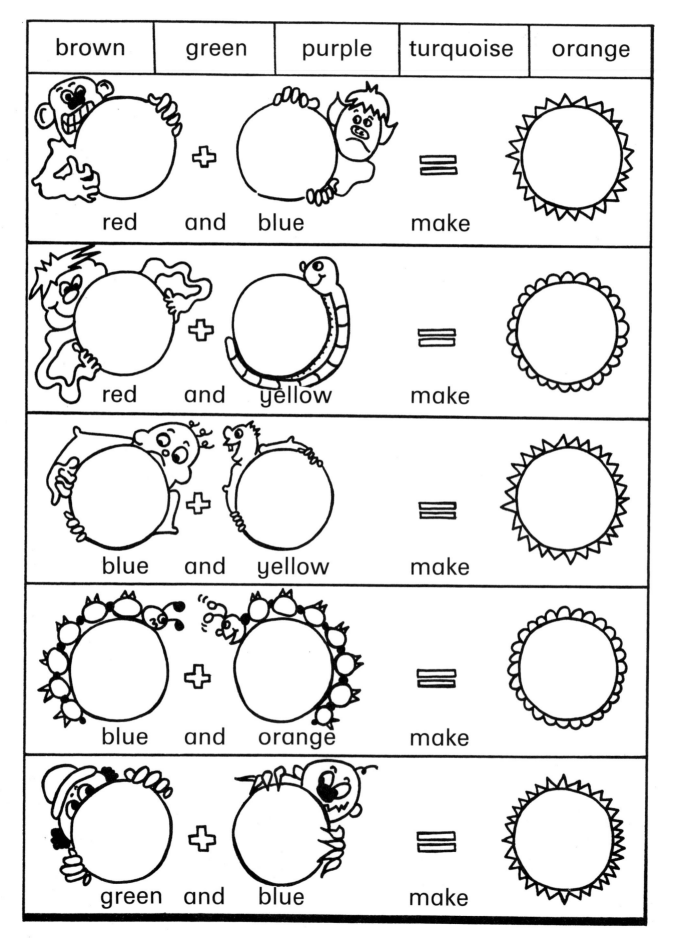

red · and · blue · make

red · and · yellow · make

blue · and · yellow · make

blue · and · orange · make

green · and · blue · make

Colours in nature

Shadows 1

Draw your shadow on the ground.

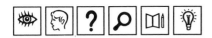
Shadows 2

Get a torch and shine it on a cup in these directions.

Draw in the  where you see it.

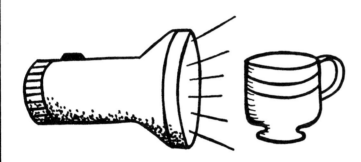

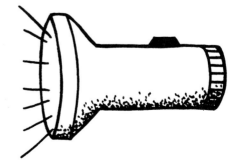

Making a sundial

We made a sundial.

We used

This is what we did.

This is how we tell the time.

Guess what

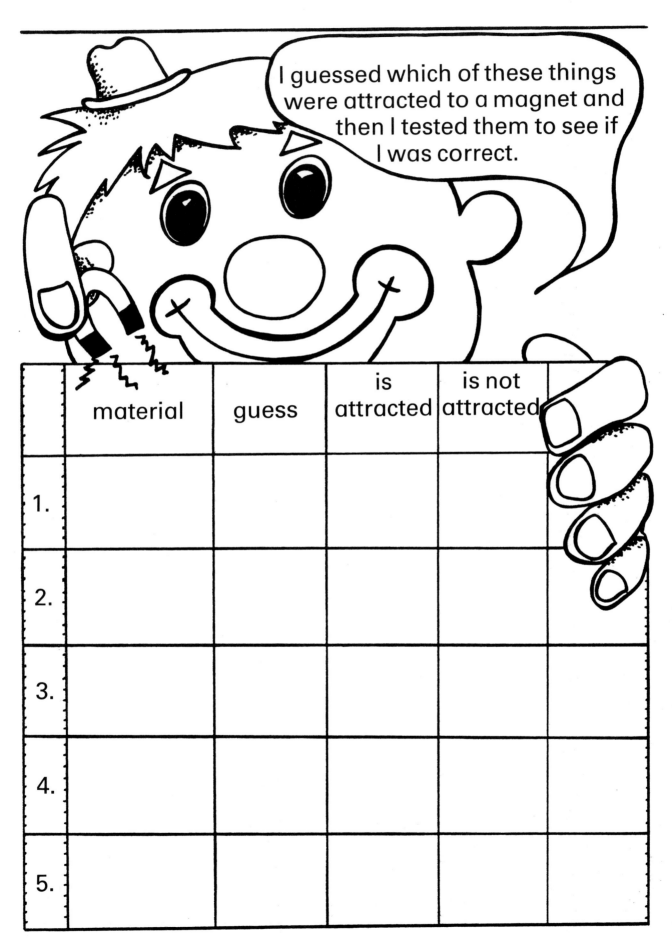

I guessed which of these things were attracted to a magnet and then I tested them to see if I was correct.

	material	guess	is attracted	is not attracted	
1.					
2.					
3.					
4.					
5.					

Magnetic poles

Hot and cold

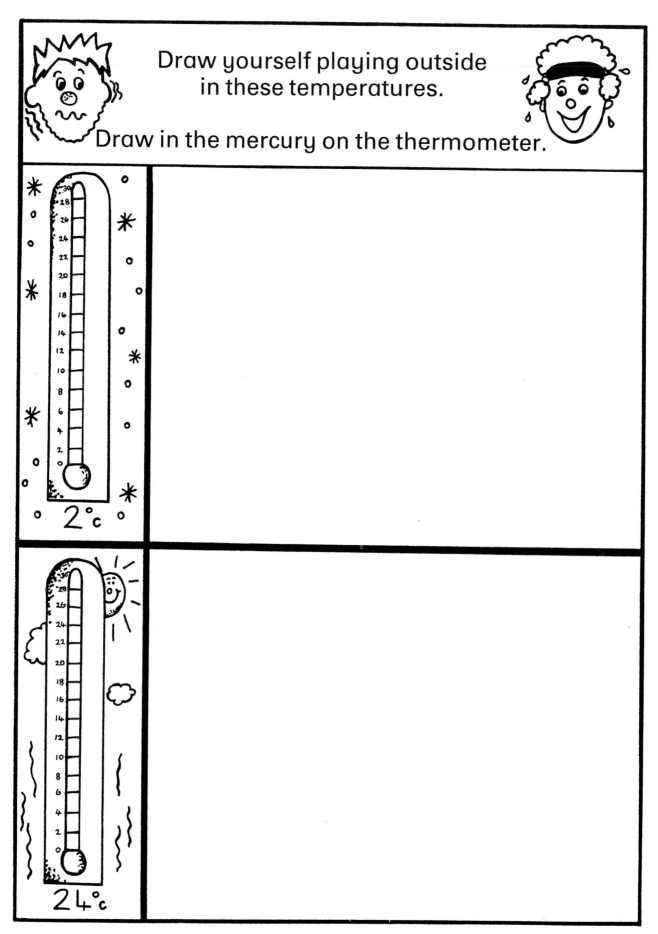

Draw yourself playing outside
in these temperatures.

Draw in the mercury on the thermometer.

2°c

24°c

Air

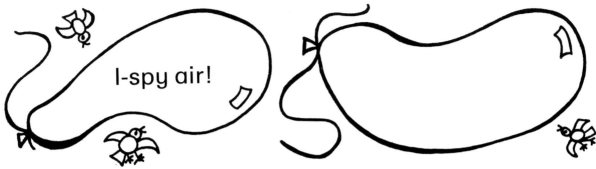

I-spy air!

1.	
2.	
3.	
4.	
5.	

How things move when pushed

 C74

How things move when pushed

object	flat surface		downward slope	upward slope — when pushing stopped		distance travelled
	gentle push	strong push		continued moving	stopped	
toy car						
doll's pram						
skateboard						
tray						
box						
block of wood						

Trying to make objects swerve

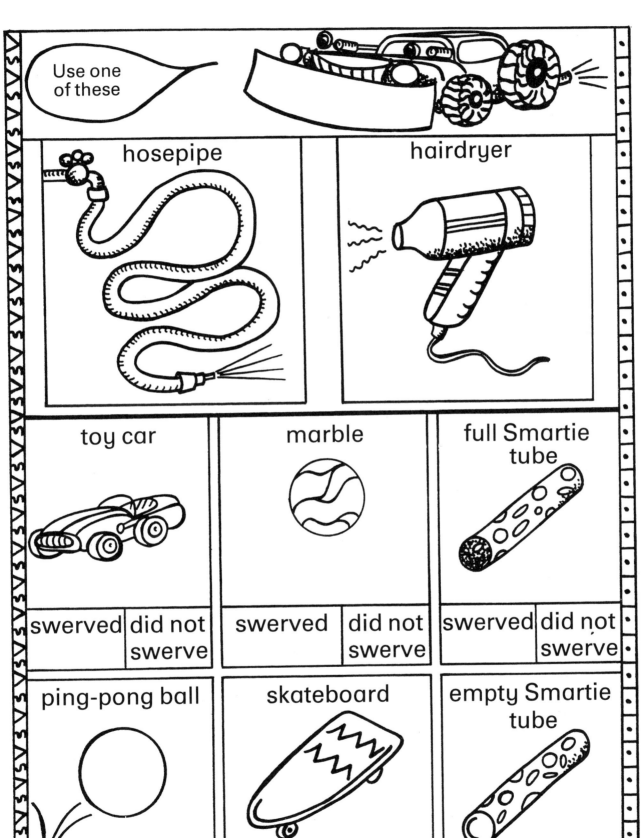

Use one of these

hosepipe

hairdryer

toy car	marble	full Smartie tube
swerved	did not swerve	swerved	did not swerve	swerved	did not swerve

ping-pong ball	skateboard	empty Smartie tube
swerved	did not swerve	swerved	did not swerve	swerved	did not swerve

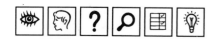

The amazing ...

This is what it looks like.

This is how I made it.

I made a ...

I made a

It looks like this.

I used these things to make it.

This is how I made it.

This is what happened when I used it.

This is how it worked.

Now you see it, now you don't

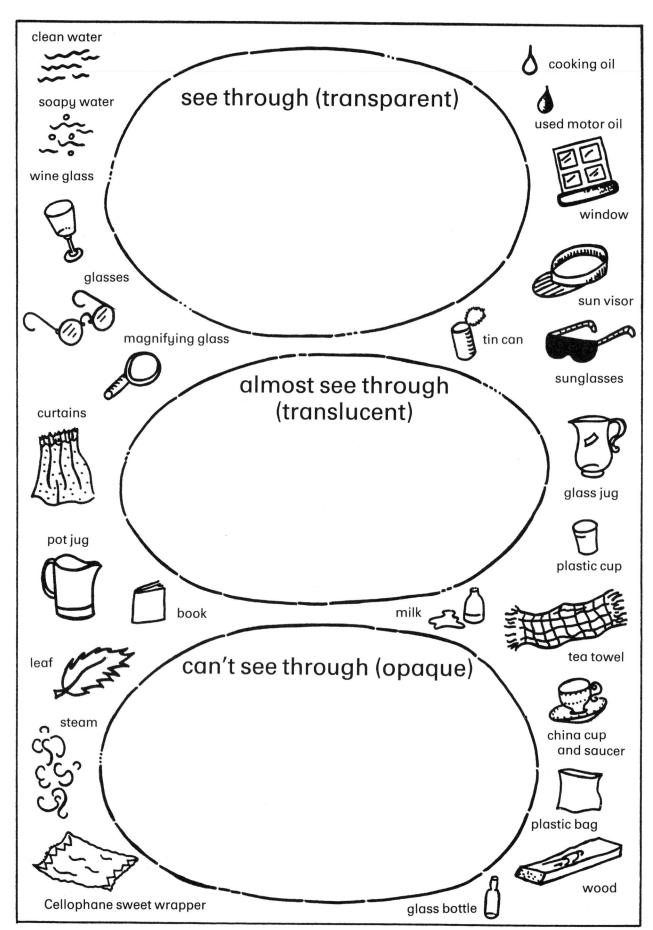

clean water

soapy water

wine glass

glasses

magnifying glass

curtains

pot jug

book

leaf

steam

Cellophane sweet wrapper

cooking oil

used motor oil

window

sun visor

tin can

sunglasses

glass jug

plastic cup

milk

tea towel

china cup and saucer

plastic bag

wood

glass bottle

see through (transparent)

almost see through (translucent)

can't see through (opaque)

Shades and shadows

Put the sun in the sky and draw the shadows where they should fall. Colour and shade the picture.

The Sun, Moon and Earth

Sun

Earth

Moon

Write in the missing words.

The ☼ _____ is a big star.

We live on planet 🜨 _____ .

The ☽ _____ goes round the Earth.

Sun ☼	Moon ☽	Earth 🜨

Why night occurs

We wanted to show why night occurs.

We used these things: _____

_____

This is what we did: _____

_____

_____

_____

_____

This is what we saw: _____

_____

After school

C82

Summer

In summer the sky is _____ when we go home from school.

Winter

In winter the sky is _____ when we go home from school.

Circuits

Fuels

gas

electricity

solid fuel

oil

solar

wood

Floating and sinking

C85

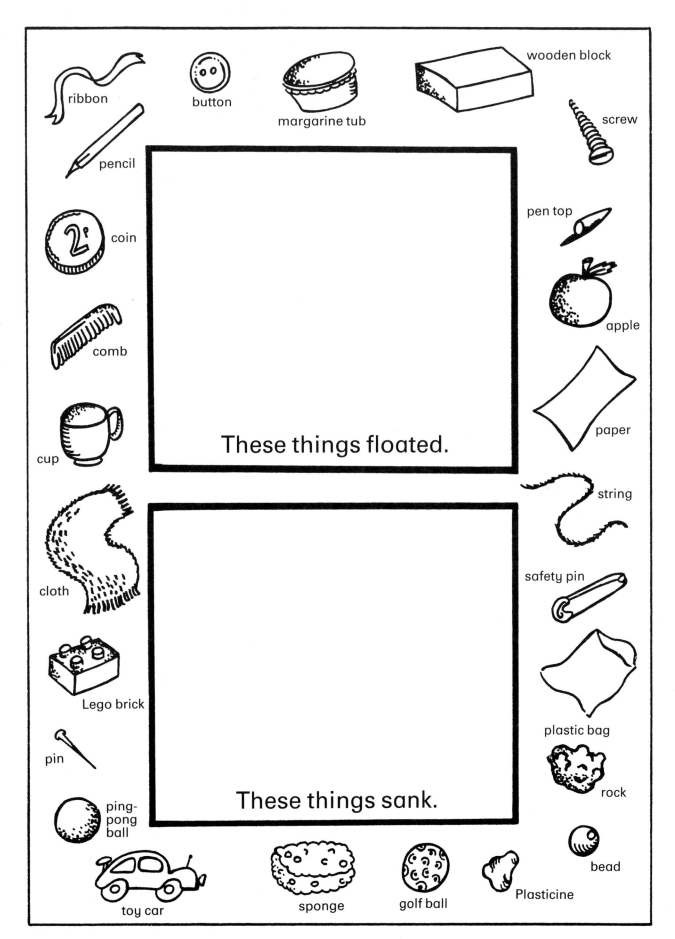

ribbon

button

margarine tub

wooden block

screw

pencil

pen top

coin

apple

comb

paper

cup

These things floated.

string

cloth

safety pin

Lego brick

plastic bag

pin

rock

ping-pong ball

These things sank.

bead

toy car

sponge

golf ball

Plasticine

Using mirrors

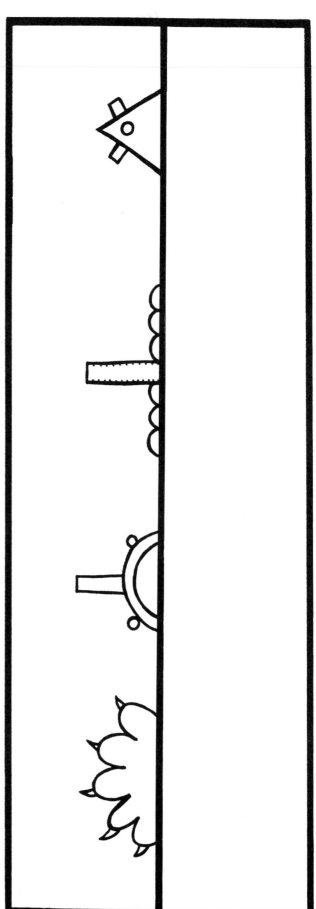

Echo survey

Place	Surfaces	Echo		
		good	fair	poor

Echo survey

What shall I wear?

A day out

Weather record

Monday			
Tuesday			
Wednesday			
Thursday			
Friday			

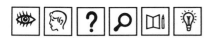
The seasons clock

 C91

W _ _ _ _ _

S _ _ _ _ _

What would you
wear in the
different seasons?

January

December

February

November

March

October

April

September

May

August

June

July

A _ _ _ _ _

S _ _ _ _ _ _

| Winter | Spring | Summer | Autumn |

Weather record

	Sunday	Monday	Tuesday	Wednesday	Thursday	Friday	Saturday
Morning							
Temperature							
Afternoon							
Temperature							

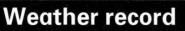

The seasons

Draw yourself having fun in each season of the year. Make sure you are wearing the proper clothes.

Changes in living things

Match the pictures to the season and complete the word.

Spring	Summer	Autumn	Winter

S _ _ _ _ _ _

S _ _ _ _ _

W _ _ _ _ _ _

A _ _ _ _ _

Record Sheets
1–6

Key Stage One AT1
Levels one and two

Name

Year/Class

A record of the number of experiences of AT1 processes.

👁	👂	?	🔍	📏	☑	✏	💡	⚠

Comments

RECORD SHEET 2: AT1

Key Stage One AT1
Level three

Name   **Year/Class**

A record of the number of experiences of AT1 processes.

H	🔍	⚖	⏱	🥤	📖✎	📊	🌀	1.2.3.4.	⚠

Comments

RECORD SHEET 3

Key Stage One

Name

Level   **Year/Class**

AT2	
AT3	
AT4	

Comments

RECORD SHEET 4

Key Stage One

Name

Level

Year/Class

AT2

Comments

RECORD SHEET 5

Key Stage One

Name

Level   **Year/Class**

AT3

Comments

RECORD SHEET 6

Key Stage One

Name

Level   **Year/Class**

AT4

Comments